CW00422288

Songs for the Church's Year

Music for the Feasts & Seasons

Dom Alan Rees

We hope you enjoy the music in this book. Further copies are available from your local music shop or Christian bookshop.

In case of difficulty, please contact the publisher direct by writing to:

The Sales Department
KEVIN MAYHEW LTD
Rattlesden
Bury St Edmunds
Suffolk
IP30 0SZ

Phone 01449 737978
Fax 01449 737834

Please ask for our complete catalogue of outstanding Church Music.

First published in Great Britain in 1995 by Kevin Mayhew Ltd

© Copyright 1995 Kevin Mayhew Ltd

ISBN 0 86209 591 3
Catalogue No: 1450025

The texts and music in this book are protected by copyright and may not be reproduced in any way for sale or private use without the consent of the copyright owner.

Front Cover: *The Miraculous Draught of Fishes*
by Zanobi di Benedetto Strozzi (1412-1468).
Reproduced by kind permission of Museo di San Marco Dell'Angelico,
Florence/Bridgeman Art Library, London.
Cover design by Juliette Clarke and Graham Johnstone.
Picture Research: Jane Rayson

Music Editor: Donald Thomson
Music setting by Kate Emerson

Printed and bound in Great Britain

Contents

Foreword

This collection of songs and psalms for the Church's year is the fruit of many years of composing music for the liturgy. Several of the pieces were written for the brethren at Belmont Abbey, Hereford, and for the boys of the Abbey School; others were written at the request of religious communities or individuals for particular feasts or occasions. They span a period of some thirty years – *Una hora* (Responsory for Tenebrae) comes from the time I was Director of Music at the Metropolitan Cathedral in Cardiff, when the Liturgy was rapidly changing.

My involvement in Cathedral and Monastic worship has given, and continues to give me, a deep love for the modal tradition of liturgical music as it comes to us in Gregorian Chant and classical polyphony. Much of my music is neo-modal in character, preserving a simplicity of style that is suitable for monastic worship. Earlier involvement in the music of the Anglican Church has also left its mark and I shall always be grateful for the opportunity of a formation in the great music of the Catholic and Anglican traditions, also in the hymn tradition of Welsh nonconformity that graced my earliest years.

Many of the songs follow the traditional form of Verse and Response, the Response being given out by a Cantor, repeated by the choir and congregation before the first verse is sung, and then repeated after every verse.

I am grateful to Alan Ridout and James O'Donnell for their helpful comments and encouragement, and to Donald Thomson, my editor. Most of this music would not have come to life but for the voices of the Belmont community and several generations of Belmont School choristers, as well as the many religious communities and others who have used it in manuscript form. I am grateful to them all.

DOM ALAN REES OSB

THE SEASON OF ADVENT

Entrance Song 1

Response To you, O Lord, I lift up my soul, I trust in you to set me free.

Verses

1. Lord, make me know your ways. Lord, teach me your paths. Make me walk in your truth, and teach me: for you are God my Sa - viour.

2. The Lord is good and up - right. He shows the path to those who stray, he

guides the hum-ble in the right path; he teach-es his way to the poor.

Text: from Psalm 24 (Grail Translation)

Gospel Acclamation

Al - le - lu - ia, al - le - lu - ia, al - le - lu - ia, al - le - lu - ia.

Show us your mer - cy, Lord, and give us your sav - ing help.

Text: Psalm 85:7

Entrance Song 2

Response Re - joice, re - joice in the Lord! Let your hearts o'er - flow with

glad - ness for the Lord is near at hand. **Verse** Cry out with joy to the

Lord, all the earth. Serve the Lord with glad - ness. Come be - fore him, sing - ing for joy.

Response: Dom Alan Rees; Verse: from Psalm 99 (Grail Translation)

Mother of Christ

for New Hall Community

Mo - ther of Christ! hear thou thy peo - ple's cry,

Text: *Alma Redemptoris Mater*, Hermann the Lame (*d*. 1054) trans. unknown

Communion Song

Response Say to the an-xious: be strong and fear not, for our God will come to save us.

Verse Strength-en the fee - ble hands, stea - dy the knees that give way, say to

those with fear - ful hearts: be strong and do not fear.

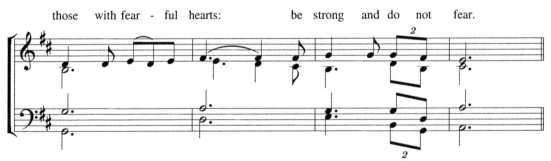

Text: from *The Roman Missal*, based on Isaiah 35:3-4

An Advent Hymn

ORIENS DCM

1. Wa - ken, O sleep - er, wake and rise, sal - va - tion's day is near, and

let the dawn of light and truth dis - pel the night of fear.

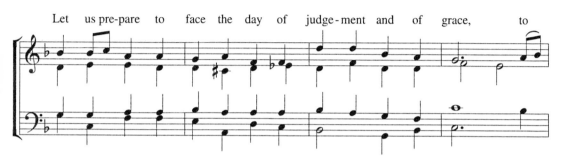

Let us pre-pare to face the day of judge - ment and of grace, to

live as peo - ple of the light, and per - fect truth em - brace.

2. Watch then and pray, we cannot know
   the moment or the hour,
   when Christ, unheralded, will come
   with life-renewing power.
   Then shall the nations gather round
   to learn his ways of peace,
   when spears to pruning-hooks are turned,
   and all our conflicts cease.

Text: Michael Forster (*b.* 1946)

An Advent Carol

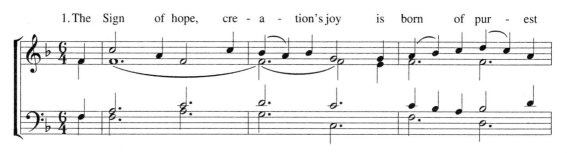

1. The Sign of hope, cre-a-tion's joy is born of pur-est

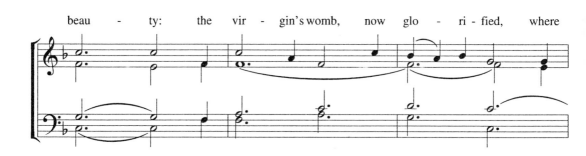

beau-ty: the vir-gin's womb, now glo-ri-fied, where

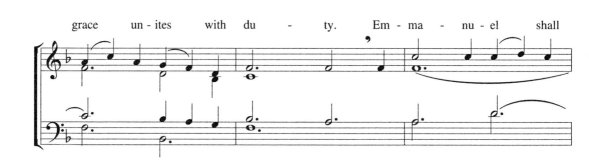

grace un-ites with du-ty. Em-ma-nu-el shall

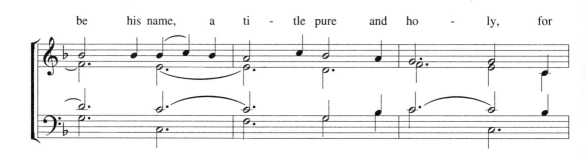

be his name, a ti-tle pure and ho-ly, for

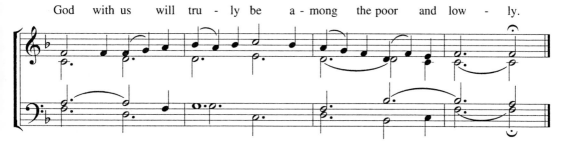

God with us will tru - ly be a - mong the poor and low - ly.

2. Where love divine concurs with trust
   to share redemption's story,
   Emmanuel in hope is born,
   and earth exults in glory.
   Now we, by grace and duty called,
   proclaim to every nation
   the Sign of hope which Mary bore,
   and promise of salvation.

Text: Michael Forster (*b.* 1946)

THE SEASON OF CHRISTMAS

A Christmas Alleluia

for Belmont Parish Choir

Bright and joyful

Al - le - lu - ia, al - le - lu - ia, al - le - lu - ia, al - le - lu - ia, al - le - lu - ia, al - le - lu - ia, al - le - lu - ia.

Glo - ry to God, glo - ry to God in the high - est heav'n and

D.C.

peace to all, peace to all, peace to all his peo - ple.

Text: Dom Alan Rees

THE SEASON OF LENT

Responsory for Ash Wednesday

Response Di-rect our hearts to bet-ter things, O Lord; heal our sin and ig-no-rance.

Lord, do not face us sud-den-ly with death, but give us time to re-pent.

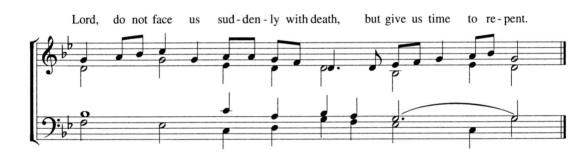

Verse Turn to us with mer-cy, Lord; we have sinned a-gainst you.

Text: from *The Roman Missal*, based on Baruch 3:5

Gospel Acclamation

Response Glo-ry to you, O Christ, you are the word of God! **Verse** Your

words are spi-rit, Lord, and they are life. You have the mes-sage of e-ter-nal life.

Text: based on John 6:63

Song of the Suffering Servant (Old Testament)

Response

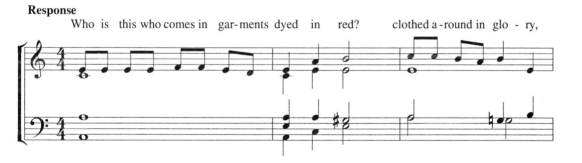

Who is this who comes in gar-ments dyed in red? clothed a-round in glo-ry,

march-ing, great in strength? It is I, says the Lord, migh-ty to save.

Verses 1. I have trod-den the wine press a - lone, no - one would stand by my

side. I looked for some - one to help, in vain I sought for sup - port.

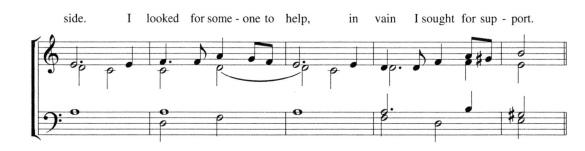

Response
Who is this who comes in gar-ments dyed in red? clothed a-round in glo - ry,

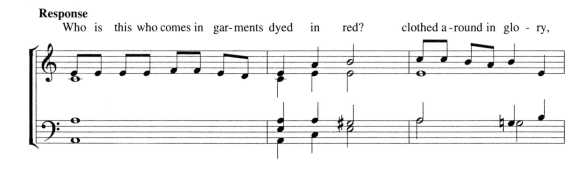

mar-ching, great in strength? It is I, says the Lord, migh - ty to save.

2. Yes, I bore all your grief and car - ried all your

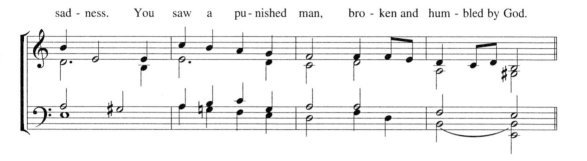

sad - ness. You saw a pu - nished man, bro - ken and hum - bled by God.

3. I was pierced through for your faults, I was crushed for all your

sins. My pu - nish-ment brings you peace, my wounds will heal you all.

4. You strayed from me like sheep, you fol - lowed your own

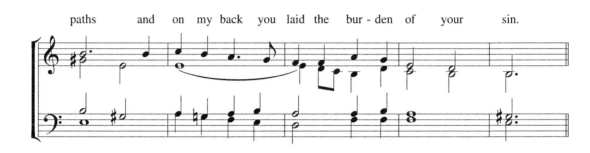

paths and on my back you laid the bur - den of your sin.

Response

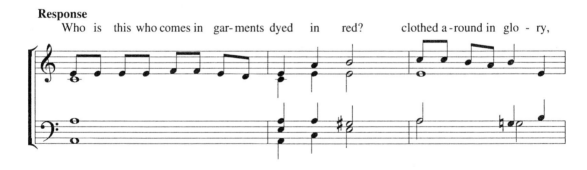

Who is this who comes in gar - ments dyed in red? clothed a - round in glo - ry,

mar - ching, great in strength? It is I, says the Lord, migh - ty to save.

5. You saw me in my grief, a Lamb for sin - ners slain; but

God has raised me up to dwell with him on high.

Response: Isaiah 63; Verses: Isaiah 53

Song of the Suffering Servant
(New Testament)

for the Ven. English College, Rome

Response By his wounds you have been healed!

Verses 1. Christ suf-fered for you, leav-ing you an ex-am-ple that you should fol-low in his steps.

2. He com-mit-ted no sin, no guile was found on his lips.

When he was re-viled, he did not re-vile in re-turn.

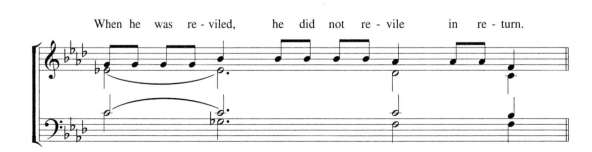

3. When he suf-fered, he did not threat-en; but he trust-ed to him who jud-ges just-ly.

4. He him-self bore our sins in his bo-dy on the tree, that we might die to sin and

live to righ-teous-ness. By his wounds you have been healed, for you were stray-ing like sheep

but have now re-turned to the shep-herd, and guar-dian of your souls.

Text: 1 Peter 2:24

Song for the Blessing of the Water

Response Give me, Lord, a new heart, put a stead-fast spi-rit in me.

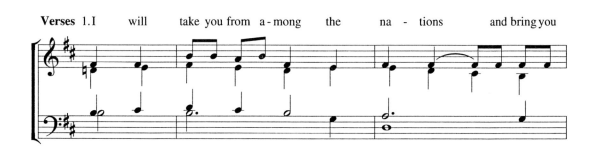

Verses 1.I will take you from a-mong the na - tions and bring you

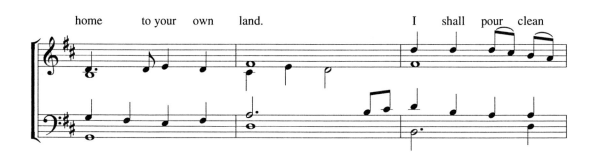

home to your own land. I shall pour clean

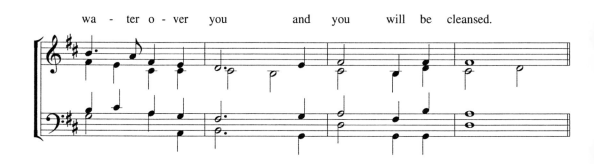

wa - ter o - ver you and you will be cleansed.

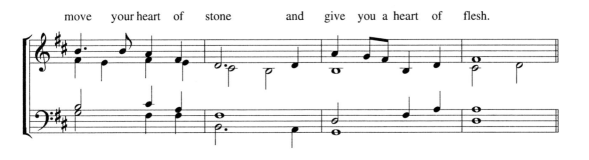

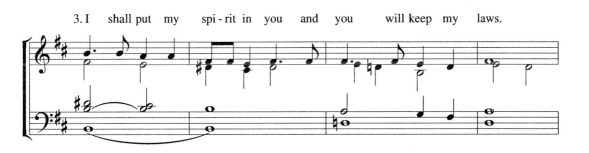

Response Psalm 51:10; Verses: Ezekiel 36:24-28 adapted by Dom Alan Rees

MAUNDY THURSDAY

Entrance Song

We pro-claim your death, Lord, un-til you come.

3. A new com-mand-ment you give to us, O Lord: 'Show

love for one a - no - ther as I have loved you.'

4. If we have died with him, then we shall live with him.

If we hold firm then we shall reign with him.

Response: from *The Roman Missal*, based on Galatians 6:14; Verses: based on John 13

Four Antiphons for the Washing of Feet

I

Response

Solo Lord, do you wash my feet? Lord, do you wash my feet?

Verses

1. Je - sus said to him: If I do not wash your feet, you can have no part with me.

2. So he came to Si - mon Pe - ter who said to him:

3. Now you do not know what I am do - ing, but la - ter you will un - der - stand.

Optional Descant

II   The Lord Je - sus, when he had ea - ten with his dis - cip - les, poured wa - ter in - to a

28

Text: from *The Roman Missal*, based on John 13; 1 Corinthians 13

Where is love and loving kindness

for the Belmont Community

Response

Where   is love   and lov-ing kind - ness,   God   is there.

Verses 1. The love   of Christ   has ga-thered us to-ge-ther in one:

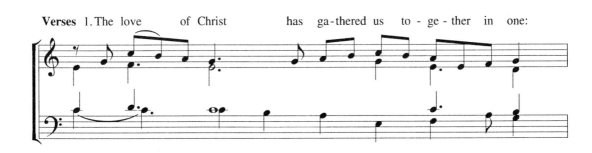

let us then re - joice   and be glad in him.

2. Let us fear and love the liv-ing God; let us love each o-ther in the depths of our hearts.

3. There-fore when we are to - ge - ther let us take heed not to be di - vi - ded in mind.

4. Let there be an end to bit-ter-ness and quar-rels, an end to strife, and in our midst be Christ our God.

5. And in com-pa - ny with the bles - sed may we see your face in glo - ry, Christ our God:

pure and un - bound - ed joy for e - ver and e - ver. A - men.

Response: Dom Alan Rees; Verses: The Bishops' Conference of England and Wales

Responsorial Psalm

for James O'Donnell, Master of Music, Westminster Cathedral

Response

cup that we bless is a com-mun-ion with the blood of Christ.

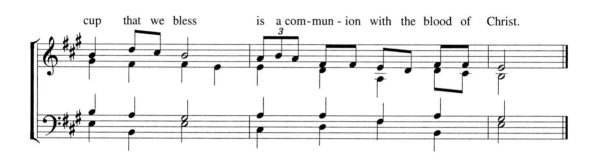

Verses 1. How can I re-pay the Lord for his good - ness to me? The

cup of sal-va-tion I will raise; I will call on the Lord's name.

This may also be used as a Communion Song at any time.

Text: from *The Roman Missal*, based on Psalm 115

Una Hora

in memory of HMR

U - na ho - ra non po - tu - is - tis

qui ex - vi - gi - la - re me - cum, qui ex -

hor - ta - ba - mi - ni
hor - ta - ba - mi - ni mo - ri pro me?

Vel Ju - dam non vi - de - tis quo - mo - do non dor - mit, sed

Translation

Could you not stay awake with me for one hour, you who were encouraging each other to die for me? Or do you not see how Judas is not asleep but hurrying to betray me to the Jews? Why do you sleep? Get up and pray not to enter into temptation.

Latin text: from *Liber Usualis*; English translation: H.J. Richards

GOOD FRIDAY

Song at the Veneration of the Cross
for the Poor Clare Community, Arundel

Christ *(Group)*

1. Look, is there sor-row like mine as wide and deep as the sea?

I am your Sun and I sink a - lone in the dark-ness of sin.

Tra - vel my pas-sion with me, I am most deep - ly a - lone.

Response

(All) Cap-tured and ha - ted and scourged are you the Lord of our joy?

*Alternative simple chordal accompaniment, originally for zither, but also suitable for guitar.

See how they mock, how they sneer at you, the Lord of our joy.

F   Dm   Em   Am   Dm   E

Christ *(Solo)*

2. I love you with love be-yond words   I washed your feet as a sign.

Soft Flute
Solo

Sw.
Strings *p*

Am   Dm   E

Sw.

I am the beau-ty you seek – de - filed and des-pised by you all.

Am   Dm   E

(to v.3)

Look at me, gaze at my face, weep at this wound in my heart.

Am   C   Dm   Am   Dm   A

This should be sung straight through, as the Response is not sung after every verse.

Mary (*Solo*)
3. My Son, I stand by your cross, far, far from that crib of our

Am   Dm   Am   Dm   Am   Em

bliss; I held you then in my arms, now you em-brace all the world.

F   (Dm)   Am   Dm   E

Christ (*Group*)
4. I am your God, and yet see no-one is poor-er that I;

Am   F   Dm   E

placed in a crib, and now see – they hang me high on this cross,

Am   Fmaj7   Em   Dm   Dm7   Am

yield-ing my heart to your love, op - 'ning my flesh to your spear.

F   Dm   Am   Em   Dm   Am

Response

(All) Cap-tured and ha - ted and scourged   are   you   the Lord of our   joy?

Am   Em   Am   Dm   Am   Am⁷

See how they mock, how they   sneer   at   you,   the Lord of our   joy.

F   Dm   Em   Am   Dm   E

Christ *(Solo)*

5. Look at these holes in my   hands,   these   hands   which mould-ed the   stars.

Flute *p*

Am   Dm   E

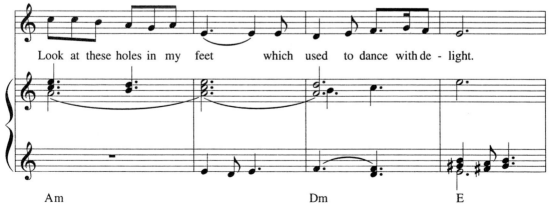

Look at these holes in my   feet   which   used   to dance with de - light.

Am   Dm   E

39

Look at the marks of the whip, look at the spit on my face.

Am C Dm Am Dm A

Mary *(Solo)*

6. My Son, I ga-ther your pain, har-vest-ing life for the

Am Dm Em   Am

world, till you, the seed, can find rest deep in the earth of my heart.

Em Dm   Em F Dm E

Christ *(Solo)*

7. See, like a mir-ror I hang; my friend, gaze long at my wounds,

poco cresc.

Am   Dm   E

deep as a well to re - fresh; my dear, I die for your love.

Am   Dm   E

See, I am trod-den like grapes crush - ing a vin - tage for you.

Am   C Dm   A

Response

(All) Cap-tured and ha - ted and scourged are you the Lord of our joy?

Am   Em   Am   Dm   Am   Am⁷

See how they mock, how they sneer at you, the Lord of our joy.

F   Dm   E Am   Dm   E

Christt *(Group)*

8. See, now I die for your love   I die, al-though I am   life.

mf meno mosso

Am   Dm   E

Wait, I will rise once a - gain.   Be - lov - ed, you will be   free.

f

Am   Em   Dm   Am

I am the frag-rance of life,   wounds are the   pride   of   my   love.

più f   *molto rit.*

F   Dm Am   Em   F Em⁷   Am

Text: Sister Frances Teresa

The Reproaches as sung at Belmont Abbey

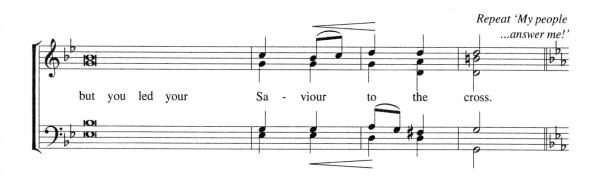

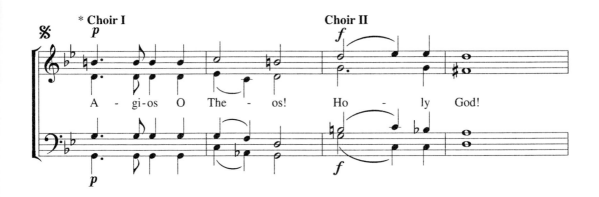

Choir I · *p* · Choir II · *f*

A - gi-os O The - os! Ho - ly God!

I *p* · II *f*

A - gi-os is - chy - ros! Ho - ly and strong!

I *p*

A - gi-os a - tha - na - tos, e - le - i-son i - mas!

II *f* · *mp*

Ho - ly im - mor - tal one, have mer - cy u - pon us!

Choir may divide into two parts as indicated by the symbols **I** *and* **II**

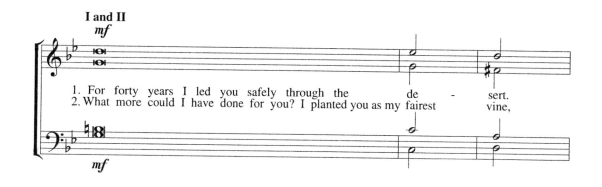

I and II

1. For forty years I led you safely through the desert.
2. What more could I have done for you? I planted you as my fairest vine,

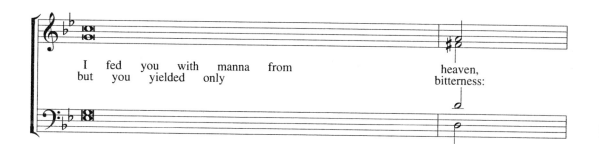

I fed you with manna from heaven,
but you yielded only bitterness:

and brought you to a land of plenty;
when I was thirsty you gave me vinegar to drink,

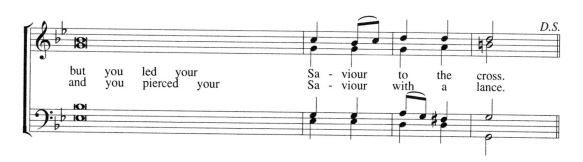

but you led your Sa - viour to the cross.
and you pierced your Sa - viour with a lance.

Text: from *The Roman Missal*

Chants at the Veneration of the Cross

Antiphon

We wor-ship you, Lord, we ve-ne-rate your cross, we praise your re-sur-rec-tion. Through the cross you brought joy to the world.

Psalm

May God be gra-cious and bless us; and let his face shed its light u-pon us.

The Reproaches

*Choir

My peo-ple, what have I done to you? How have I of-fend-ed you? an-swer me! I led you out of E-gypt, from sla-ve-ry

*Repeat 'My people
...answer me!'*

to free-dom, but you led your Sa-viour to the cross.

Choir   **with Congregation**

I A-gi-os O The-os. Ho-ly is God.

Choir may divide into two parts as indicated by the symbols **I and **II***

46

Choir

with Congregation

II A - gi - os is - chy - ros! Ho - ly and strong!

Choir

I A - gi - os a - tha - na - tos, e - le - i - son i - mas!

with Congregation

I,II Ho - ly im - mor - tal one, have mer - cy on us!

Choir

I,II For forty years I led you safely through the desert.

I fed you with manna from heaven, and brought you to a land of plenty;

Repeat 'Agios O Theos'

but you led your Sa - viour to the cross.

Choir

I,II What more could I have done for you?

I planted you as my fair - est vine, but you yielded

only bit - ter - ness: when I was thirsty you gave me vinegar

Repeat 'Agios O Theos'

to drink, and you pierced your Sa - viour with a lance.

Text: from *The Roman Missal*

VIGIL

Baptismal Song

Bless - ed be God, bless - ed be God, bless - ed be

God who has cho - sen you.

Unison

Re - joice, you new - ly bap - tised, cho - sen

mem - bers of the king - dom bur - ied with Christ in

poco rit.

death you are born a - gain with him in faith!

poco rit.

a tempo

49

Text: from *The Roman Missal*

Like the deer

Response

Like the deer that yearns for run-ning streams, so my soul is yearn-ing for you, my God.

Verses

1. My soul is thirst - ing for God, the God of my

life; when can I en - ter and see the face of God?

2.These things will I re - mem - ber as I pour out my soul: how I would lead

the re - joic - ing crowd in - to the house of God, a - mid cries of

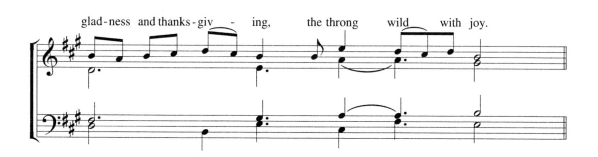

glad - ness and thanks - giv - ing, the throng wild with joy.

Text: from *The Roman Missal*, based on Psalms 41 and 42

THE SEASON OF EASTER

Easter Response

for New Hall Community

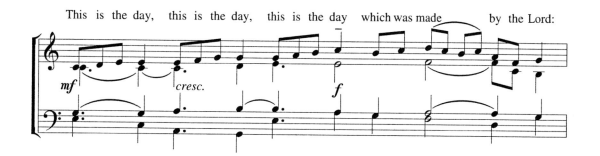

Text: from *The Roman Missal*, based on Psalm 117

Processional Song

CHARLBURY GROVE 888 and Alleluias

Come let us praise our ri-sen Lord, from his pierced heart is love out-poured, and through that love is life re-stored, Al-le-lu-ia, al-le-lu-ia, al-le-lu-ia.

2. Sing out the joy of victory
by the Lord's wounds are we set free,
healed and restored on Calvary,
Alleluia, alleluia, alleluia.

3. Worthy is he, to him we sing,
   our Paschal Lamb, pure offering,
   to him our thanks and praise we bring,
   Alleluia, alleluia, alleluia.

4. You passed through death that we might live,
   to that great love our hearts we give,
   Lord by your Blood, our sins forgive.
   Alleluia, alleluia, alleluia.

DOXOLOGY – after any section

All praise to God the source of Light,
praise to the Spirit, glory bright,
praise to the Son who conquers night,
Alleluia, alleluia, alleluia.

PRESENTATION OF THE GIFTS

1. We bring you gifts, our wine, our bread,
   may they be blessed and we be fed,
   may they be Christ who rose from the dead.
   Alleluia, alleluia, alleluia.

2. We have drawn near from east and west,
   to honour Christ our victim blest,
   in his great love may all find rest,
   Alleluia, alleluia, alleluia.

3. Worthy is he, to him we sing,
   our Paschal Lamb, pure Offering,
   he is the praise and thanks we bring.
   Alleluia, alleluia, alleluia.

COMMUNION

1. I am your Bread, the victim blest,
   come eat and drink this Paschal feast,
   come to my peace for I am rest,
   Alleluia, alleluia, alleluia.

2. I am your Way, your Truth am I
   I am your Life, I will not die,
   Light on the road and always nigh,
   Alleluia, alleluia, alleluia.

3. I am your Shepherd, tender, true,
   have no more fear, I call to you,
   follow my voice, your life renew,
   Alleluia, alleluia, alleluia.

4. I am your Peace, my love receive,
   open your heart and now believe,
   your sins and sorrow I relieve,
   Alleluia, alleluia, alleluia.

5. I am the First, the Last am I,
   eat of my bread and never die,
   live evermore with me on high,
   Alleluia, alleluia, alleluia.

Text: Sister Frances Teresa

THE SEASON OF PENTECOST

Come, Spirit of Our God

1. Come, Spi - rit of our God, our lives with truth in - spire, and burn with - in our fear - ful hearts like pu - ri - fy - ing

fire.

cresc.

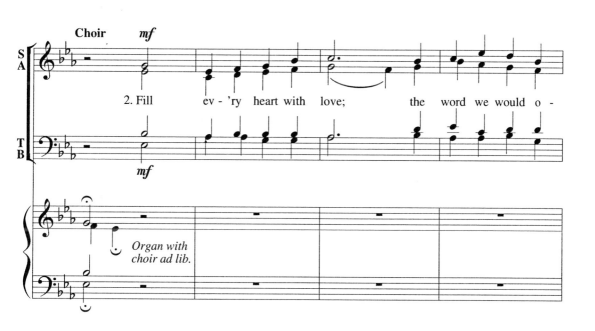

Choir *mf*

2. Fill ev - 'ry heart with love; the word we would o -

mf

Organ with choir ad lib.

bey. O teach us all we need to know of your most ho - ly

way.   3. Come   with the

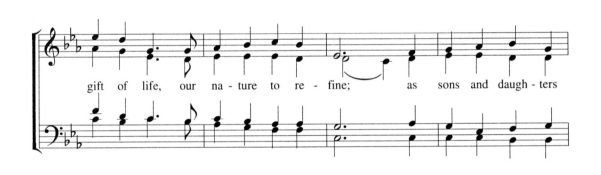

gift of life, our na - ture to re - fine;   as   sons and daugh - ters

let   us   live,   and heirs of love   di - vine.

Slightly slower

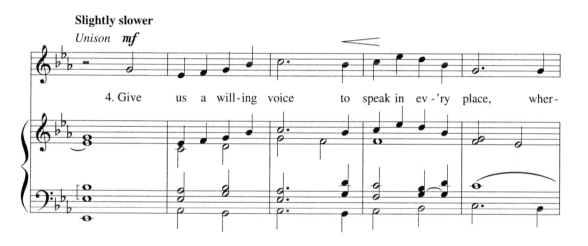

4. Give us a will-ing voice to speak in ev-'ry place, wher-

e - ver doubts and fears con-fine, of li - be - ra - ting grace.

Text: Michael Forster (*b.* 1946)

THE TRINITY

Behold the Glory

MYSTERY PROFOUND 86 88 66

Unison Be - hold the glo - ry long con-cealed, though to the pro - phet shown;

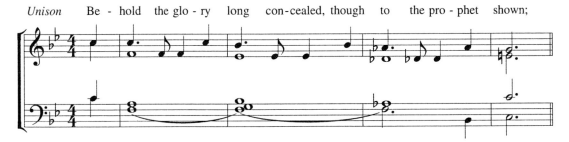

Harmony in dark my - ste - rious cloud once sealed, this ma - jes - ty is

now re-vealed to mor - tal sight made known, to mor - tal sight made known!

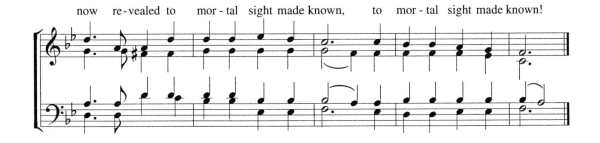

2. The Father of eternal love
   his Son incarnate gave,
   with grace and glory from above,
   death's final curtain to remove
   and Adam's children save,
   and Adam's children save.

3. With joy and praise, eternally,
   creation will resound,
   to Father, Son and Spirit, three,
   one undivided Trinity,
   O Mystery profound,
   O Mystery profound!

Text: Michael Forster (*b*. 1946)

CORPUS CHRISTI

Holy God

LIVING BREAD 84 84 88 84

Con brio

Ho - ly God, your pil - grim peo - ple by you were fed, through the vast and dread - ful des - ert guid - ed and led; wa - ter from the rock-face pour - ing, hope to ev - 'ry heart re - stor - ing, sets the fail - ing spi - rit soar - ing, life from the dead.

2. Living bread for mortals broken,
   gift from above,
   live in us the life eternal,
   perfect in love.
   Come, the word of wholeness bringing,
   where our fearful souls are clinging;
   and of life abundant singing,
   all fear remove.

3. One the bread and one the chalice,
   one work of grace;
   one the church of Christ, united
   in his embrace.
   One the gospel of salvation,
   for the wholeness of creation:
   Christ is poured in ev'ry nation,
   and ev'ry race.

Text: Michael Forster (*b.* 1946)

I love you, Lord

for Dom Ralph Wright

CARITAS CM

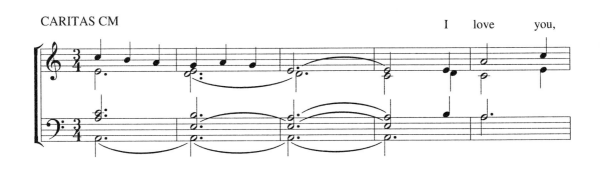

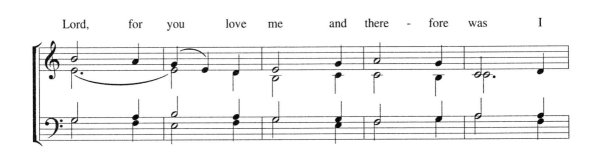

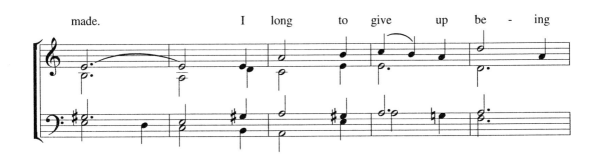

2. I long to give you everything
   that you have given me:
   in giving all I find your will
   and thereby am made free.

3. To love you, Lord, with all my heart
   is freedom, pure, supreme:
   in giving this you give me all
   without this all is dream.

Text: Dom Ralph Wright OSB

FEASTS OF THE BLESSED VIRGIN MARY

Hail, Holy Queen

for New Hall Community

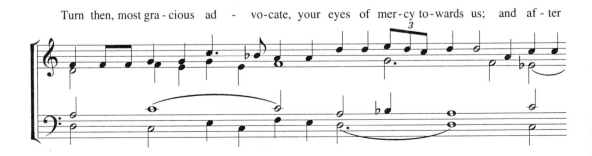

This anthem may be sung after Night Prayer during Ordinary Time.

this our ex - ile show un - to us the bless- ed fruit of your womb, Je - sus.

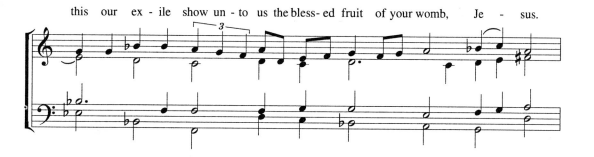

O cle - ment; O lov - ing; O sweet vir - gin Ma - ry.

Text: Traditional

PSALMS

Glorify the Lord

for Abbot Mark Jabalé

Not hurried, with breadth

*Response

Glo - ri - fy the Lord with me and let us ex - alt his name.

Choir

Verses 1. I will bless the Lord at all times, his praise al - ways on my lips; in the Lord my soul shall make its boast. The hum - ble shall hear and be glad.

*The Response should be given out by a Cantor and repeated by All in unison.
It may be sung in harmony on further repeats.*

2. Look t'wards him and be ra - diant; let your faces not be a - bashed. Taste and see that the Lord is good. You are hap-py and safe in him.

Choir
Unison
3. Come, chil-dren and hear me, let me teach you the fear of the Lord.

Harmony
Turn a - side from e - vil and do good;

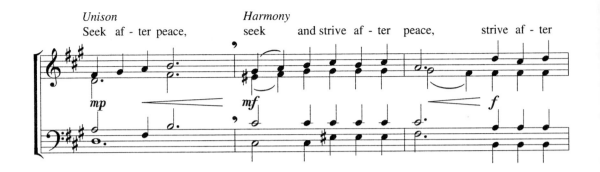

Text: from Psalm 33 (Grail Translation)

Go out to the whole world

for Dom Nicholas and Dom John

Harmony ad lib.

out to the whole world, pro - claim the Good News!

The heav'ns pro-claim the glo - ry of God and the

fir - ma - ment shows forth the work of his hands.

Harmony ad lib.

Day un - to day takes up the sto - ry and night un - to

night makes known the mes - sage.

Go out to the whole world, pro - claim the Good News!

Unison
meno f

No speech, no word, no voice is heard yet their span ex -

tends through all the earth, their words to the ut - most bounds of the world.

Harmony ad lib.
Go

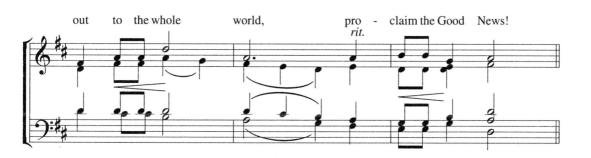

out to the whole world, pro - claim the Good News!

Text: from Psalm 18 (Grail Translation)

The Lord will bless his people

Response

The Lord will bless his peo - ple, he will bless his peo - ple with peace.

Verses

1. O praise the Lord, you chil - dren of God. Hon - our his

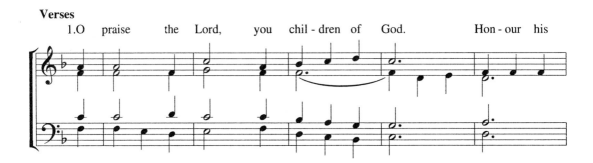

glo - ry and pow'r. Praise the glo - ri - ous

name of the Lord, wor - ship his ho - li - ness, kneel and a - dore.

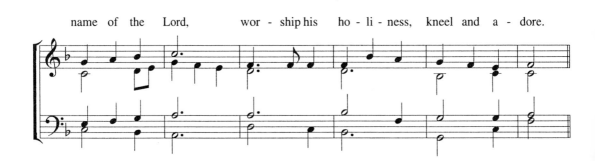

2. The voice of God re-echoes around,
   thunders on waters and oceans.
   Strong and mighty his powerful voice,
   full of his majesty, splendour and grace.

3. The voice of God splits light'ning apart;
   'Glory!' they cry in his temple.
   God, enthroned over tempest and flood,
   rules as our king through all ages to come.

Optional Descants
Response

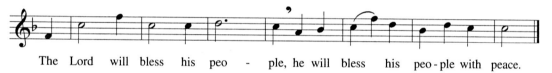

The Lord will bless his peo - ple, he will bless his peo-ple with peace.

Verse 3

The voice of God splits light-'ning a - part; 'Glo - ry!' they

cry in his tem - ple. God, en - throned o - ver

tem - pest and flood, rules as our king through all a - ges to come.

Text: Susan Sayers, based on Psalm 28

Come, children and hear me

for Ealing Abbey Community

Response

Come, chil-dren and

hear me and I will teach you the fear of the Lord.

Verses 1. I will bless the Lord at all times, his praise al-ways on my lips; in the

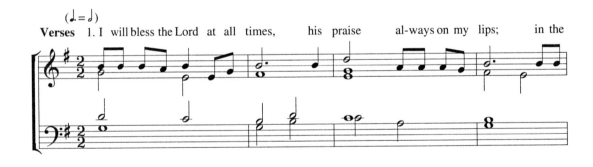

Lord my soul shall make its boast. The hum - ble shall hear and be glad.

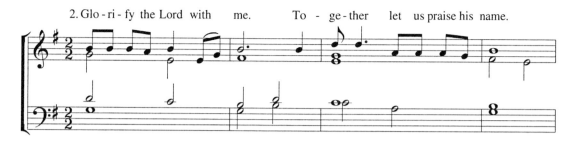

2. Glo - ri - fy the Lord with me. To - ge - ther let us praise his name.

Look t'wards him and be ra - diant; let your fa - ces not be a - bashed.

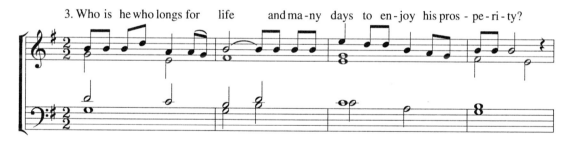

3. Who is he who longs for life and ma - ny days to en - joy his pros - pe - ri - ty?

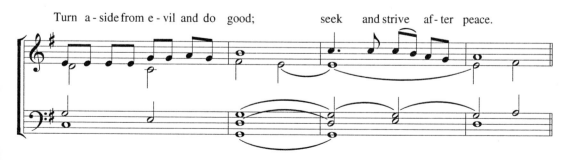

Turn a - side from e - vil and do good; seek and strive af - ter peace.

Text: from Psalm 33 (Grail Translation)

They are happy, who dwell in your house *for Dom Brendan, Dom Martin and Dom Matthew*

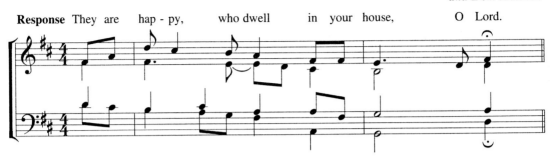

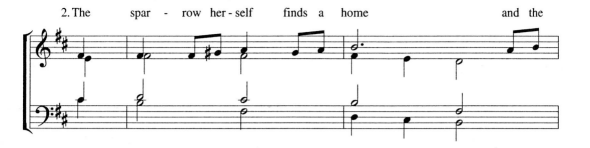

2. The spar - row her - self finds a home and the

swal - low a nest for her brood; she lays her young by your

al - tars, Lord of hosts, my king and my God.

3. They are hap - py, who dwell in your house, for e - ver sing - ing your

praise. They are hap - py, whose strength is in

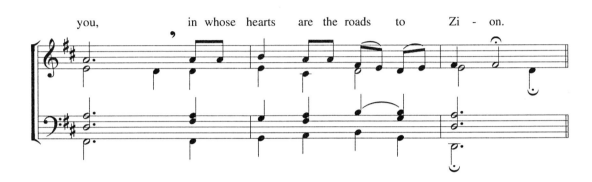

you, in whose hearts are the roads to Zi - on.

Response

They are hap - py, who dwell in your house, O Lord.

4. One day with - in your courts is

bet - ter than a thou - sand else - where. The thres-hold of the house of

God I pre - fer to the dwel-lings of the wick - ed.

Text: from Psalm 83 (Grail Translation)

Acknowledgements

The publishers wish to express their gratitude to the following
for permission to reproduce copyright text material:

The Bishops' Conference of England and Wales, 39 Eccleston Square, London
SW1V 1PD for *Where is Love and Loving Kindness* © 1966.

The International Committee on English in the Liturgy, Inc (ICEL),
1234 Massachussetts Avenue NW, Washington DC 20005, USA
for the English translation of 'The Reproaches' from
The Rite of Holy Week © 1972 ICEL, and the English translation
of 'Blessed be God' from *The Rite of Baptism for Children* © 1969 ICEL.
Used by permission. All rights reserved.

Sister Frances Teresa OSC, Convent of Poor Clares, Crossbush, Arundel,
Sussex BN18 9PJ for the *Arundel Reproaches* and *An Easter Entry*
© Copyright Community of Poor Clares.

A.P. Watt Ltd, 20 John Street, London WC1N 2DR on behalf of
The Grail, England for extracts from Psalms 18, 24, 33, 83 and 99,
taken from *The Psalms: A New Translation,* published by HarperCollins Ltd.

Dom Ralph Wright OSB, St Louis Priory, 500 South Mason Road,
St Louis, Missouri 63141, USA for *I Love You, Lord.*

All other texts and music in this book are the copyright of Kevin Mayhew Ltd,
and may not be reproduced in any way without the express permission
of the copyright owner. It is illegal to photocopy music.